THE JAMES GALWAY FLUTE COLLECTION

18 Galway Editions for Flute by 13 Composers

ISBN 978-1-4234-8297-0

G. SCHIRMER, *Inc.*

DISTRIBUTED BY

HAL•LEONARD®
CORPORATION

7777 W. BLUEMOUND RD. P.O. BOX 13819 MILWAUKEE, WI 53213

www.schirmer.com
www.halleonard.com

JAMES GALWAY EDITIONS FOR FLUTE
G. SCHIRMER

COLLECTIONS

Golden Moments for Flute and Piano	50482479
Joy to the World	50335400
Songs for Annie	50335060
Three Nocturnes for Flute and Piano	50507610

JOHANN SEBASTIAN BACH

Concerto for Flute in A Minor	50336040
Suite in B Minor for Flute with Piano Reduction	50481083

FRANÇOIS BORNE

Fantaisie Brillante on Themes from Bizet's Carmen	50336050

ANTONÍN DVOŘÁK

Sonatina for Flute and Piano, Op. 100	50480055

CHARLES GRIFFES

Poem for Flute with Piano Reduction	50481637

ARAM KHACHATURIAN

Three Pieces for Flute and Piano	50480024

WOLFGANG AMADEUS MOZART

Concerto for Flute in G Major, K. 313	50481087
Concerto for Flute in D Major, K. 314	50481086
Andante for Flute and Piano in C Major, K. 315	50481085

CARL REINECKE

Sonata for Flute and Piano (Undine), Op. 167	50336260

HEITOR VILLA-LOBOS

Arias from Bachianas Brasileiras No. 5	50226900

ANTONIO VIVALDI

Spring from the Four Seasons	50506750
Summer from the Four Seasons	50506760
Autumn from the Four Seasons	50506770
Winter from the Four Seasons	50506780

CONTENTS

JAMES GALWAY BIOGRAPHY

Sir James Galway is regarded as both the supreme interpreter of the classical flute repertoire and a consummate entertainer whose appeal crosses all musical boundaries.

As one of the most recorded classical artists performing today, Sir James has made himself a legend, a modern musical master whose virtuosity on the flute is equaled only by his limitless ambitions and vision. Through his extensive touring, over 30 million albums sold and his frequent international television appearances, Sir James has endeared himself to millions worldwide. As an instructor and humanitarian, Sir James is a tireless promoter of the arts.

As he approaches his 70th birthday, Sir James continues to look for new and innovative approaches to music and to life. For O'Reilly Street, recorded on the Sony Classical label, Galway performs music from the jazz suites of Claude Bolling with the addition of Afro Cuban percussion. Collaborating with him on this new album is two-time Grammy nominated Cuban music group, Tiempo Libre, known for its sizzling timba music. The recording is rich in the traditions of multiple genres, authentic yet emotionally seductive, and woven with threads of classical, jazz and Cuban music. Sir James will perform selections from the album with Tiempo Libre at Ravinia in 2009.

Sir James, his wife renowned flutist Lady Jeanne Galway and harpist Catrin Finch, transported listeners on a journey through the works of Wolfgang Amadeus Mozart on his album My Magic Flute. He continues to delight fans through the RCA Red Seal album The Essential James Galway (May, 2006) featuring selections ranging from Peer Gynt and Concertino for Flute and Piano, Op. 107, to The Girl from Ipanema and Riverdance.

Other recent albums include Ich war ein Berliner: James Galway and the Berlin Philharmonic and Wings of Song, as well as his performances on the soundtrack to The Lord of the Rings: Return of the King. A discography of over 60 CDs with BMG Sony Classics reflects his mastery of musical diversity.

In September 2008, Sir James opened the New York Philharmonic's season, their last under the baton of Maestro Lorin Maazel, with a concert and PBS special "Live from Lincoln Center," which Sir James also hosted. This was followed by a special guest appearance on the PBS Special "The Priests," filmed in Northern Ireland. Other U.S. highlights of this season include performances with the Chicago, Boston, Nashville, Long Island, Austin and Spokane and York Symphonies. Joined in recital, Sir James and Lady Jeanne Galway will delight audiences with pianist Christopher O'Riley in North American cities ranging from Houston, TX, to Mesa, AZ and Waterloo, ON.

Other International concerts include recitals in Paris, France; CRR Concert Hall in Istanbul, Turkey; the National Concert Hall in Dublin, Ireland and the UK. Particular highlights include a tour with the Israel Camerata Jerusalem of Israel, Spain and Switzerland; filming, recording and concert tour with I Solisti Veneti in the Palazzo Ducale in Venice and throughout Italy; Special Performance with Maestro Lorin Maazel and the Philharmonia Orchestra in London, Cardiff and Barcelona, performing Maestro Maazel's concerto for Flute, written for Sir James.

Belfast born, Sir James went on to study in London and Paris before embarking on his orchestral career in such prestigious orchestras as the Sadlers Wells and Royal Covent Garden Operas, The BBC, Royal Philharmonic and London Symphonies, before taking up the coveted position of solo flautist with the Berlin Philharmonic under Herbert Von Karajan.

Since 1975, when Sir James launched his solo career, he has continuously performed with the world's leading orchestras and conductors, participated in chamber music engagements, popular music concerts and given master classes. From Galway's lips have come definitive treatments of classical repertoire and masterworks by Bach, Vivaldi, and Mozart. He also features contemporary music in his programs, including new flute works commissioned by him and for him by composers such as Amram, Bolcom, Corigliano, Heath, Lieberman and Maazel.

Sir James has played for such dignitaries as Queen Elizabeth II, Pope John Paul II, President Clinton, President George W. Bush, President George H.W. Bush, President Mary McAleese, Prince Charles, HRH The Princess Royal, The Empress of Japan, The Queen of Norway, Princess Diana, TRH The Earl and Countess of Wessex, TRH The Duke and Duchess of Kent, and most recently President Shimon Peres, and shared the stage with an amazing array of entertainers including Stevie Wonder, Henry Mancini, John Denver, Elton John, The Chieftains, Ray Charles, Joni Mitchell, Jessye Norman, Cleo Laine and Andrea Bocelli. He performed with Pink Floyd in their memorable concert at the Berlin Wall, was part of the Nobel Peace concert in Norway and performed at the G Seven summit hosted by Queen Elizabeth II in Buckingham Palace.

Alongside his busy performing schedule he finds time to share his wisdom and experience with the generations of tomorrow by conducting annual master classes, commissioning new works for the flute, publishing articles, books and flute studies. Both Sir James & Lady Galway undertake the running of their International Flute School in Weggis, Switzerland, each summer, which gives them the opportunity to personally nurture students of all levels. His website www. thegalwaynetwork.com is devoted to all students, educators and flute lovers worldwide.

Sir James devotes much of his free time supporting charitable organizations such as SOS, FARA, Future Talent, Swiss Artistic Foundation, The Caron Keating Foundation and UNICEF, with which he holds the title of special representative. Sir James continues to be honored for his accomplishments. He was inducted in the Hollywood Bowl Hall of Fame in June 2008 and was the recipient of the 2008 UMS Distinguished Artist Award at the 13th Annual Ford Honors Program. Irish America Magazine also awarded Sir James and Lady Jeanne Galway the "2008 Spirit of Ireland," award recognizing them for their roles as musical ambassadors.

Sir James was named the 1997 Musician of the Year by Musical America and has received Record of the Year awards from Billboard and Cash Box magazines, as well as the Grand Prix du Disque for his recordings of the Mozart Concerti. His 60th birthday was commemorated with 1999's Sixty Years, a 15-CD retrospective of his works for the RCA Victor Red Seal label.

Her Majesty Queen Elizabeth II of England has honored him twice: in 1979 with an Order of the British Empire and in 2001 with a Knighthood for services to music. In 2004, Sir James was given the President's Merit Award from the Recording Academy at the Grammy's 8th Annual "Salute to Classical Music." He has also been honored at the prestigious Classic Brits Awards held in London's Royal Albert Hall in 2005, where he received the coveted "Outstanding Contribution to Classical Music" award in celebration of his 30 years as one of the top Classical Musicians of our time.

Bourée I and II
from Orchestral Suite No. 2 in B minor, BWV 1067

Piano Reduction by Phillip Moll

Johann Sebastian Bach
(1685–1750)

BOURRÉE I

BOURRÉE II

Bourrée 1 da capo

Polonaise and Double
from Orchestral Suite No. 2 in B minor, BWV 1067

Piano Reduction by Phillip Moll

Johann Sebastian Bach
(1685–1750)

POLONAISE
Lentement

DOUBLE

Polonaise da capo

Minuet in G Major
from Six Minuets, WoO 10, No. 2

Piano Transcription by Phillip Moll

Ludwig van Beethoven
(1770–1827)

Fantaisie Brillante
on themes from the opera *Carmen* by Georges Bizet

Piano Part Edited by Phillip Moll

François Borne
(1840–1920)

20

Habanena
Allegretto quasi andantino

VARIATION 1

VARIATION 2
Lento

Chanson de Bohème et Final

Gavotte in D Major

Piano Transcription by Phillip Moll

François-Joseph Gossec
(1734–1829)

Ave Maria
adapted from the first prelude of J. S. Bach

Piano Transcription by Phillip Moll

Charles-François Gounod
(1818–1893)

Andante con moto

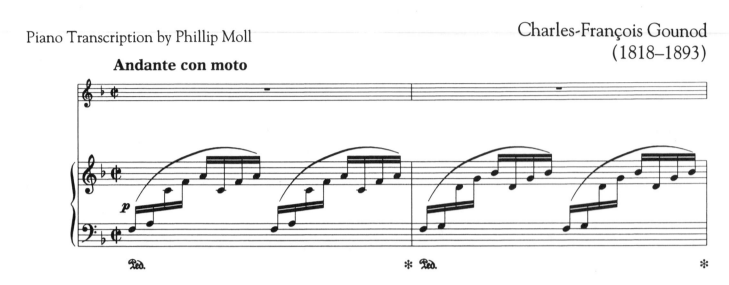

pedale sempre simile

* At m. 17 and again at m. 19, Gounod indicates a *subito* *p* following the *crescendo* in the preceding measure. I prefer a gradual tapering to *piano*. —J. Galway

* Optional: piano part one octave higher until ** m. 39 (two measures from end).

Poem
for Flute and Orchestra

Piano Reduction by Phillip Moll

Charles T. Griffes
(1884–1920)

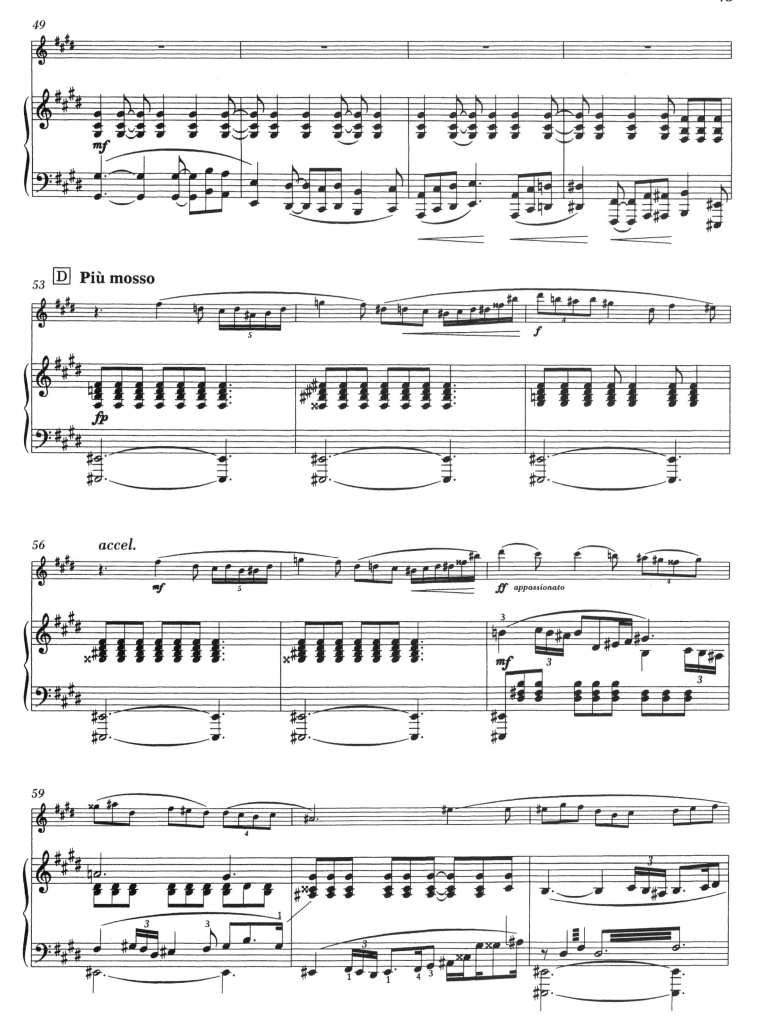

H **Allegro scherzando**

Tambourin

Piano Reduction by Phillip Moll

Johann Adolf Hasse
(1699–1783)

Le Basque
from Book Four of *Pieces for Viol*

Piano Reduction by Phillip Moll

Marin Marais
(1656–1728)

Serenade
second movement from String Quartet in F Major
Op. 3, No. 5

Piano Transcription by Phillip Moll

Franz Joseph Haydn
(1732–1809)

Allegro maestoso
first movement from Concerto in G Major
for Flute and Orchestra, K. 313

Piano Reduction by Phillip Moll

Wolfgang Amadeus Mozart
(1756–1791)

212

216

Allegro aperto
first movement from Concerto in D Major
for Flute and Orchestra, K. 314

Piano Reduction by Phillip Moll

Wolfgang Amadeus Mozart
(1756–1791)

*) ossia:

Irish Tune from County Derry

Piano Reduction by Phillip Moll

Traditional

Allegro
first movement from Sonata (Undine), Op. 167

Piano Reduction by Phillip Moll

Carl Reinecke
(1824–1910)

*The hand-crossings are suggested by Reinecke. The editor prefers
to play both of these notes with the right hand.

Allegro
first movement from Violin Concerto in E Major
"La primavera," Op. 8, No. 1

Piano Reduction by Phillip Moll
Spring has returned.

Antonio Vivaldi
(1678–1741)

SONG OF THE BIRDS

All is gay, and the birds sing happily.

FLOWING FOUNTAINS
Fountains play in the breeze, constantly moving.

THUNDER

The skies are dark; lightning flashes and thunder roars.

SONG OF THE BIRDS
After the storm, the birds return with their song.